EMPOWERED
2022

POWERFUL VOICES

Edited By Iain McQueen

First published in Great Britain in 2022 by:

Young Writers
Remus House
Coltsfoot Drive
Peterborough
PE2 9BF
Telephone: 01733 890066
Website: www.youngwriters.co.uk

Printed and bound in the UK by BookPrintingUK
Website: www.bookprintinguk.com
YB0MA0005H

⋆ FOREWORD ⋆

Since 1991, here at Young Writers we have celebrated the awesome power of creative writing, especially in young adults where it can serve as a vital method of expressing their emotions and views about the world around them. In every poem we see the effort and thought that each student published in this book has put into their work and by creating this anthology we hope to encourage them further with the ultimate goal of sparking a life-long love of writing.

Our latest competition for secondary school students, Empowered, challenged young writers to consider what was important to them. We wanted to give them a voice, the chance to express themselves freely and honestly, something which is so important for these young adults to feel confident and listened to. They could give an opinion, share a memory, consider a dilemma, impart advice or simply write about something they love. There were no restrictions on style or subject so you will find an anthology brimming with a variety of poetic styles and topics. We hope you find it as absorbing as we have.

We encourage young writers to express themselves and address subjects that matter to them, which sometimes means writing about sensitive or contentious topics. If you have been affected by any issues raised in this book, details on where to find help can be found at www.youngwriters.co.uk/info/other/contact-lines

✳ CONTENTS ✳

Eden Boys' School, Bolton

Muhammad Umar Patel (12)	39
Mohammed Amaan Malatgar (12)	40
Abdullah Dudhiya (12)	41

Greenford High School, Southall

Imaan Asim (12)	42
Rohan Singh (13)	43
Sanaya Shalley (13)	44
Rooda Ahmed (13)	46
Tilakshan Rasikanthan (13)	47
Karina Khar (13)	48
Hawlat Bilal (13)	49
Abdulbasit Bakhshi (12)	50
Jahish Sayanthan (11)	51
Frances Hartnett (13)	52
Anmol Sarna (11)	53

Hammersmith Academy, Shepherd's Bush

Ashleigh Doba-Bishop (12)	54
Eileen Tazarkesh (12)	55
Deksan Guelle (11)	56
Leonard Owedye (11)	57
Mariam Kouira (11)	58
Leticia Delfina (11)	59
Darne Zewldi (12)	60

Haydon Secondary School, Eastcote

Ella Williams (12)	61
Kayden Yeung (13)	62
Lily Norbury (15)	63

Heath Park School, Wolverhampton

Leah Clarke (15)	64
Sophia Parveen (16)	65
Simran Kaur (12)	66

Jashandeep Kaur (12)	67

Kirk Hallam Support Centre, Kirk Hallam

Michael Musgrave (11)	68

Madrasatul Imam Muhammad Zakariya School, Bolton

Khadijah Sufi (14)	69
Juyrah Hosain (12)	70
Sasabil Zait (12)	72
Unaisah Patel (12)	74
Aaisha Malji (14)	75
Maryam Akram (12)	76
Bareerah Sadick (12)	77

Maidenhill School, Stonehouse

Katie Moray (12)	78
Megan Vaughan (13)	79
Maxine Strode (11)	80
Isaac Page (13)	81

North Herts ESC, Hitchin

Robert Clark (13)	82
Ellie-May D (14)	83

Rainford High School, Rainford

Esme Michalec (11)	84
Levi Shaw (11)	86
Francesca Jones (12)	87
Poppy Foster (13)	88
Isabella Green (12)	89
Leila Bouhnassa (13)	90
Holly Herrington (15)	91
Kali Guinness (11)	92

Ranelagh School, Bracknell

Ella Davey (15)	93

St Bernard's Catholic Grammar School, Slough

Gabi Howe (16)   96

St Catherine's College, Armagh

Eabha McConnell (13)   98

St Malachy's High School, Castlewellan

Beth Kerr (14)   99
Ciara Cartwright (14)   100

Stanborough School, Welwyn Garden City

Emily Turner (14)   101
Tianna Parmley (13)   102
Oliver Kyriacou (13)   103
Matthew Ives (14)   104

Summerhill School, Kingswinford

Esme Garrington-Naylor (11)   105
Lucie Evans (12)   106

The Manor Academy, Mansfield Woodhouse

Tyler Stocker (12)   107
Isabelle Walker (12)   108
Charlotte Hunt (12)   110
Denis Josu   111
Nicola Bird (12)   112

The Sacred Heart Language College, Wealdstone

Savannah De Sa Pinto (12)   113
Maisie Joyce-Gourey (11)   114
Simran Kaur Dhami (14)   115
Francesca Wozniak (11)   116
Esioneh Adjerese (13)   117
Inieya Haroon (11)   118

Caitlin Byrne (14)   119
Fathimaladana Jawahirismail (11)   120
Alyssa Patel (14)   121
Teodora Olariu (12)   122
Ashita Bhuva (11)   123
Jennifer Adubofour (12)   124
Gabriela Kaczorowska (12)   125

The Winsford Academy, Winsford

Isabel Heywood (13)   126
Bob Ross (14)   127
Layla Ventre (13)   128
Maisie Middleton (13)   130
Adam Rowntree (13)   131
Cody Elliot (12)   132

Torquay Boys' Grammar School, Torquay

Lucas Tottman (12)   133
Felix Kelly (12)   134
Tyler Piercey (12)   135
Joe Day (12)   136
Jaden Sanders-Yeoman (12)   137
Isaac Rollings (11)   138
Hoyt Spencer (12)   139

Wembley High Technology College, Wembley

Aryan Vekaria (12)   140
Waled Alsabah (11)   141
Daria Maxinese (12)   142

THE POEMS

Teacher

If I were prime minister for a day
I would make everybody pay
I would make school seven days a week
To make kids weep
If anyone had fun
They would be done
I would make people moan and groan
I will make people sad
Because all the things I do are bad
As the people cry and sigh
I will feel all high and mighty
But then the people get fed up
They set up a plan to beat me up
I go where they want me to go
They shoot me with a big blow
Then I woke up and realised
I am probably too sinister
So that's why I am not the prime minister.

Isla MacRae

Football

I am not good at football,
That is what people call me,
I'm only there for them,
That is what they say to me.
They say because I playing in goal I'm an idiot,
They never believed in me,
Because I let in one important goal,
I'm bad.

But I believed I could do well,
I was picked last in school football,
Because they called me the geek and teacher's pet,
But I believe I can be the best.
I'm not bad,
I'm trying my best so surely I'm the best I can be,
They say I'm pathetic,
Because of one time.

I need to overcome the fright,
I need to go against their laughter,
I need to work hard,
I need to work against the impossible,
I can do this.

Eventually, people will appreciate me,
I need to work,
I believe.
Eventually, people will appreciate me;
I need to work,
I need to believe.

Dylan Baker-Newman (13)

Admiral Lord Nelson School, Portsmouth

Organ Donation Saves Lives

Organ donation saves lives,
I am living proof,
My stomach works now but back then it wouldn't,
I play football now but once I couldn't,
Your liver, your kidneys, your eyes and your heart,
Are no good when buried, so give someone a good start.

Organ donation saves lives,
I am living proof
Thank you to the child I never met,
The child that saved my life,
Thank you for the gift of life,
I cannot thank you enough.

Organ donation saves lives,
I am living proof,
Thank you NHS,
For all the work you have done,

Organ donation saves lives,
I am living proof.

Jude Allen (11)
Admiral Lord Nelson School, Portsmouth

Just 'Cause

Just 'cause they're black
Just 'cause they don't do something you like
Just 'cause they're not the same

Just 'cause their skin is a different colour
Just 'cause they haven't got the same hair colour
Just 'cause they are wearing something different on their face
Just 'cause they like the same gender

Sometimes, someone is different.
It really doesn't matter.

Henley Neill (13)
Admiral Lord Nelson School, Portsmouth

When I Was Younger

When I was younger
I had a bear
The bear I won
Was from a machine
The machine was in an arcade
There was a burning candle
The burning-bright candle was lit
I was playing with my bear
Then my bear was burning bright
I was sad and scared
I loved my bear
I stashed it in my room
And it's still lying there today
Hiding under my bed
Waiting for it to decay.

Connor Bushell (12)
Admiral Lord Nelson School, Portsmouth

Fruit Salad

Fruit salad is amazing
I love the health
Don't waste your food
It's delicious
The sweetness of fruit
The variety of salad
The wonderful simplicity
Fresh from the fridge
Like a gift from the heavens
Descended from above
Let it roll down your throat
Feast on the juices
The world's best snack.

Austin Milner (12)
Admiral Lord Nelson School, Portsmouth

Friends Are Like A Party

Friends are like a party
some come early and help put things together
some are on time and come for the fun
and laughs
some come late and make some memories.
But once the party is over
the ones who stay later to clean up messes
they didn't make true friends because
even though they didn't have anything to do with it
they helped.
That type of friend is rare.

Eva Leigh Nixon (12)
Aldercar High School, Langley Mill

Empowered

E nergy - what we love to learn.

M icroscopes - use them for cells, have no concerns.

P ower - use it on a daily basis, we know all its dangers.

O xygen - to have power in our bodies, the one thing we share with strangers.

W ater - for hydration, the hydrosphere and our underwater creatures.

E cosystem - to protect our world, we need to look after it and all its features.

R adiation - the energy from sources, from space, at the speed of light.

E vaporation - a liquid to a gas? That can't be right!

D on't be disheartened if you don't get it right, but everyone should feel powerful, because even the world is.

Kaitlyn McLellan (11)
Baines High School, Poulton-Le-Fylde

The Change I Want To See In The World...

One day the world I live in will have equal rights.
One day the world I live in will have electric cars safe for the environment and gas-powered vehicles will cease to exist.
One day the world I live in will be more green than grey.
One day the world I live in will be powered by solar power.
One day the world I live in will be free from global warming.
One day the world I live in will be free from Covid-19.
One day the world I live in will have leaders, not bosses.
One day the world I live in will be filled with kindness and not hatred.
One day the world I live in will not have dictators but only democracy where the people can choose.
One day the world I live in will not have homework.
One day the world I live in will start school at 9:45 and end at 3:30.
One day the world I live in will not have to endure the pain of pollution.
One day the world I live in will not need prisons, locks or security.
One day the world I live in will not need degrees but only curiosity and creativity since after all curiosity is the fuel that truly powers our civilisation and creativity is the evolution of our Earth.

One day the world I live in will have an empowered child that will grow up to cure cancer.
Be the change you want to see in the world.

Antonis Emmanouel (12)

Barnwell Middle School, Shephall Green

It Gets Better

Dear past me,
Maybe you're feeling so down right now
But it gets better.
Maybe you are getting bullied
But I promise it doesn't stay like this forever.
Don't be afraid to tell people how you feel
Maybe the stress gets too much however
And you turn into a mess
But maybe you're not that clever
But it gets better!

Honey Mcdonnell (13)
Barnwell Middle School, Shephall Green

Music Is My Passion

M usic is my passion
U nlike any other.
S inging is another.
I t can never be rationed.
'C ause I love it so much!

Nabhan Jaloud (14)
Barnwell Middle School, Shephall Green

Actions

People act how they want
People think how they want
Anyone can be anyone
Anyone can act
But your actions are what make you... you.

Luke Dollin (13)

Barnwell Middle School, Shephall Green

Social Setback

One hour leads to two, then two leads to three,
We scroll on our phones as a way to flee,
We don't even once just look up and see,
The amazing world around you and me,
"How about you go and visit your buddy?"
"I'd rather stay and stare at my screen."
That's the reply you give to your family,
How long until we finally agree,
That our phones are not the core of humanity?

Humanity is wonderous, you can't deny,
We've created ways to travel and fly,
We help others when they start to cry,
Yet we always return to our phones to hide,
It's time that we get up and start to try,
To do something without meaningful lives,
So, get up, and enjoy the night sky.

Amy Nelson (13)
Beauchamps High School, Wickford

Empowered

You are strong,
You are brave,
You are adventurous,
You are amazing,
Love yourself.

You have a beautiful soul,
You have a beautiful heart,
You are a beautiful human,
Love yourself.

Don't cover yourself up,
Empower yourself,
Don't hide from the crowd,
Empower yourself,
Don't pretend to be who you're not,
Empower yourself.

Everyone is different,
Like a strawberry,
All shapes and sizes,
All different colours,
Not everyone is perfect,
Except you.

Love yourself,
Love your surroundings,
And love your people.

Lacey-Faith Gunns (14)

Beauchamps High School, Wickford

Empower

E ver more the world is destroyed,

M ade by global warming we try to avoid,

P eople throwing all into a pollution void.

O ver 14 million tons of plastic ends up in the ocean each year,

W here you can see if you stand at the end of a pier,

E verywhere it is found, over there, over here.

R ound the world it flows through the sea.

Grace Kersey (12)

Beauchamps High School, Wickford

I Am A Woman

I'm the female lead, I'm the female lead,
With a female body and a female head.

I don't want to hear that I talk like a man,
Because I am sure about the things I've said.

There's nothing manly about confidence,
There's nothing manly about competence.

My experience and my dominance shouldn't be diminished,
If only when I'm wearing a dress,

The only difference is documents with letters M or F,
And the consequent subconscious opposite creates
hypotheses that are just excuses.

Like 'men are from Mars and women are from Venus'?
We're not from another planet because we can grow a
foetus.

But it's socially acceptable to stomp out uniqueness,
When the prophets profit off of sweetness and weakness.

Men are our CEOs and presidents and heroes,
They are our role models and saviours like Jesus,

Why can't we ever let a woman think she's a genius?
Why can't we ever let a woman be the boss?
Why can't we ever let a woman take charge?

Emily Howell (12)
Brentwood School, Brentwood

Empowered

I'm just a lonely girl in a lonely world,
But deep down there's a part that speaks.
I'm just a ball of emotions, tight and furled
That can't roar but only squeak.

But under all that shy and timidness,
There's a star in the darkness.
And it's burning bright, full of happiness,
Showing my courage and confidence.

And it's gonna flood the dam of insecurity,
Gonna rise and show who's boss.
It's gonna conquer all of my obscurities,
And go and slash and tear them with my claws.

And I don't care what anybody says,
They can laugh and jeer if they want.
But when I'm a queen I'll go and end their days,
And it's my name they'll chant.

Though I'm a lonely girl in a lonely world.

Anushka Kishore Kumar (12)
Brentwood School, Brentwood

Am I Good Enough?

Am I good enough?
Wear make-up,
Fix your hair,
Cover up.
What a nightmare.

You eat too much,
You wear too much make-up,
You are too skinny,
You're too ugly, no guy would ever like you.
So many yous but what about me?

Sit, walk and talk like an angel,
Perfect smile, perfect face and perfect body,
If you're not perfect you're ugly and different.
Who doesn't want to be significant?

Be popular, nobody wants to talk to a weirdo
Stay out of the crowd you are too relevant
Speak louder you're too quiet.
Shut up, no one asked or cares
I just want to be me.
Am I good enough?

Tito Phillips (12)
Brentwood School, Brentwood

Future

Dear future me,
Yes, I'm going to change,
Yes, I'm going to get more friends,
Yes, I'm going to move house,
Yes, I will grow,
And yes, people will pass away,

No, I don't hate myself,
No, I won't move on,
No, I don't want to die,
I will see you in a few years,
Goodbye for now.

Cameron Hannah (13)
Broadwater School, Farncombe

Who Are You?

Your mind is like art
Everyone has a different style, perspective
Other people may not like your style, that doesn't matter
You might not like their style, but you be who you want to
be

Your style is different and unique
But you like it, you like it
Or, you may not, but you need to believe in the world
Most of all, yourself

You are strong and independent
You can pick up a pencil and create a fantasy
You can pick up a pencil and create a world, your world
You can do anything, you just have to believe

Although sometimes, when you struggle
You can ask for help
Because sometimes in your lifetime
Help is just the thing you need

So, as I read this aloud, my final words are
To not be ashamed, of who you are
Because who you are is the most important thing about you
So never forget this as I say
Your art style is your mind and your thoughts.

Isabelle Deere (12)
Campsmount Academy, Norton

Empowered

Your mind is like art,
You just follow your heart,
We all love flowers,
We wish we had powers.

Going to the gym makes you strong,
Your muscles may not be long,
Not everyone likes to read a book,
Ask for help, especially when you're stuck.

Even if you get pulled down, still follow your dream,
There may be places where not everyone has been,
Everyone loves money,
My favourite animal is a bunny.

Not many people have a house,
I love playing on keyboard and mouse,
I'm sure everyone has had luck,
My phone nearly got taken.

I'm sure people may have broken glasses,
Not many men have lasses,
I give you hope,
Unless you can already cope.

Not many people have a shoe,
My little brother is only two,
I wish I could keep my brother in a box,
I'm not scared of a fox.

Ryley Cooke (11)

Campsmount Academy, Norton

Just Be You

You don't have to be skinny
You can't always be pretty
You don't need to dye your hair
Just be you

You don't have to wear make-up
You don't need to break up
You don't need to be happy
Just be you.

Macy Deere (11)
Campsmount Academy, Norton

Football Is My Life

Football is my life
My passion
My dream, my desire
When I'm down, football helps me up
Football isn't just my sport, it's my socialisation
Football brings out the inner me
The competitive me, the better me
Friends have become family through football
Every game I play is life
Standing on the pitch, waiting for the game to start
In every weather
Sunny, cold, rain, snow
I'm nervous
I'm shivering
The game kicks off, everyone is confident
There is no better feeling than scoring a last-minute winner
Every time you win
You get closer to winning the league
Football is my life
What inspires me
What empowers me.

Mason Jenner (11)
Conisborough College, Catford

Me

T oo much chocolate
O ne more, please
M any to choose from
M any to see
Y ummy chocolate, great to see

B ounty, Twix and Mars
A ll the flavours I like
K eeps me happy
E verybody needs chocolate
R eady to eat.

Tommy Baker (11)

Conisborough College, Catford

I Am Me

I am me, I am beautiful, I am unique
I am happy, I am me, I am loved
This is me
My friends love me and we are happy
I am loving and I am me
I am respectful and caring
I am me.

Taylor Robinson (12)
Conisborough College, Catford

Your World

Think of a world,
Where everyone is respected.
Gender, religion, culture,
No one is affected.

Go deeper into your vision,
And make a decision.

Think, this is your world,
What do you want it to be?
Let your imagination go free,
That is the key.

This is your world,
So broaden your mind,
And think of a world that is your kind.

Look deep into your imagination,
And make a creation,
That you want for the next generation.

Think of a world with no global warming,
Without Coronavirus,
You're here to inspire us.

Zohaib Khan (12)
Eden Boys' Leadership Academy, Manchester

Be Empowered

Empowered means taking control over our lives
we all need to be the people, the people who strive
we all need to rise from the pain
to find the strength, to prolong all the shame
remember who you really are
don't ever hide the scar
we are all human
just like me and just like you
some might speak English, Arabic or Urdu
let your true spirits come to light
even if you are black, brown or white
don't hide your identity
be yourself because you don't live for an eternity
this is what empowered means
to be your true self and to be freed.

Ayan Tofiq (12)
Eden Boys' Leadership Academy, Manchester

Empowered

'Terrorist', 'dangerous', 'risky', 'unsafe'
A 'threat'
A 'menace'
This is how society perceives me
Perceives us
Perceives Islam
One group acts
The rest is blamed

They try painting your image
Don't listen
Paint your own self
Anything you wanna be
Paint yourself with creativity
Set yourself free
Embrace your true reality

Don't take the blame
When you're dead in your grave
Only Allah can save you
It is my religion
This is what empowers me.

Khassim Murid Sharif Mohamed (12)
Eden Boys' Leadership Academy, Manchester

Global Warming

There's pollution around us,
no solution for us,
we all are delusional,
this is the conclusion.

We all must stop this,
it's hurting lots of things,
there is a whole list,
of things that are dying.

Plants are dying,
animals are crying,
birds aren't flying,
oceans are drying.

Ice is melting,
penguins have felt it,
no one's helped it,
plants have met it.

We should help it,
get away from everything,
but people let it,
pass through us all.

Yousaf Azhar (11)
Eden Boys' Leadership Academy, Manchester

Our World

Our world is our world
no one can change it
except someone who stands up to change it

the people who are doing bad things to the Earth are bad,
if they don't stop, the tsunami will eat us now.
The Earth is also harming us by making big or small
earthquakes.
Because of that, people use more things to rebuild.
Our life is like a chocolate box,
when you finish it, you get a new one,
but our world can finish us in one second
by anything.
Everyone needs to stop dangerous things they are doing.

Harshil Sankhla (12)
Eden Boys' Leadership Academy, Manchester

All Lives Matter

People who have so much money
but don't share with the poor,
people who are filled with greed grow up
looking at what they don't have,
yet... they don't notice that
some people will be more than happy to
have what you already own.

So don't let them down, don't be lazy,
get up and support them, think as
if you were them, would you be fine?
Become someone who will save the
future of the poor.

You and I, both, need to help them.

Abdul Rafhy Shaikh (12)
Eden Boys' Leadership Academy, Manchester

Like A Piece Of Pie

Who am I?
I am me!
Like a piece of pie,
And I am free.
Like a snowflake,
I can fly with imagination.
Don't be like Blake,
Who quit the generation.
He couldn't stand it,
Too much pressure.
He fell in a jet-black pit,
Your soul's your treasure.
Now, empower others!

Bilal Maqsood (11)
Eden Boys' Leadership Academy, Manchester

Sensation

We all want a sensation,
but we can't find the destination,
we wait until the application,
we might also get detention,
or isolation,
it's your decision,
to stay on supervision,
or you can do revision,
to get an education,
and make a sensation.

Mueez Baig (12)
Eden Boys' Leadership Academy, Manchester

Footballer President

Football insprires me.
No, no, no!
I'm like Ronaldo!
Dribbling people like Ronalhino,
defending like Roberto.

If I were president for one day,
would change all the rules
and stop world hunger and
poverty.

Mujib Mirzai (11)
Eden Boys' Leadership Academy, Manchester

Be The Difference In The World

Be the difference in the world.
Motivate, don't discriminate and you'll be powerful.
Illuminate the world.
Mobilise, don't prevaricate and you'll be magical.
Be the difference in the world.
Strive and survive, and you'll stand out from the rest.
Be the difference in the world.
Don't be the one that hopes and dreams but is never focused and determined.
Once again, be the difference in the world,
Thank you.

Muhammad Umar Patel (12)

Eden Boys' School, Bolton

Empowered

You gave me life, you gave me hope
You opened up a pathway full of dreams and goals
And for that, I want to say
Never give up and lead the way

You gave me ambition and joy
And started the life of the boy I am today
Which made me cheer and made me feel
Like an array of those who you have made
And for that, I want to say
Never give up, and lead the way.

Mohammed Amaan Malatgar (12)
Eden Boys' School, Bolton

My Inspirer, My Life

You gave me life, you gave me hope
You helped me fight, you helped me cope
You rescued me when I was stuck in what felt like an endless hole
Without a doubt, you're my undying hero

You made me believe, you made me achieve
You healed my sores, you gentled my course
Without a doubt, you're my undying hero.

Abdullah Dudhiya (12)
Eden Boys' School, Bolton

Break Free

If even in the midst of flowing time,
You could feel chains holding you down for a non-existing crime,
If you were spinning round and round on an infinite carousel,
Wondering if you're a monster without a soul,
If you have two seconds to think before you sink,
And the east becomes the west,
And the dark becomes the light,
And if you are senseless as the day plunges into night,
Would you keep your sight sealed?
Would you be scared to take flight?

This is the life for many of us, but
The fretful, billowing wind pushes the eagle higher.
There is calm before the storm,
Cruelty in the norm.

Before dawn is the darkest hour,
It is just a plant before the flower,
Feel empowered.

Break free of fate.
Break free of chains.
Break free of society.

Imaan Asim (12)
Greenford High School, Southall

Empowered

Football empowers me,
Football is a part of my life that I practise every day.
Football is something I don't give up on and eventually get my pay,
Football is something I can do to make my family proud,
So that I don't end up looking like a clown.

Never give up on something you love,
Because you never know what may come from the heavens above,
Never look down,
Don't give in to that frown.

Take a deep breath
And get your crown,
Set a goal to fulfil,
Make your family proud.

Surprise those two-faced crowds,
Make the disbelievers believe
And don't concede,
Believe.

Rohan Singh (13)
Greenford High School, Southall

Empowered

Empowered in me
Empowered in my thoughts
Empowered in my dreams

No one can stop me
Break me
Tear me down
'Cause I choose and craft who I am

I don't stay quiet because I'm scared
I stay quiet because I've got better things to do
Better things to say

Listen
You are who you choose to be
Your name
Race
Religion
Gender
Can't define you

Society throws
Expectations
Not encouragement
Why?

You don't need anyone to tell you
What you can
Or what you can't do
You can do it
Not your status
Your race or religion
Your gender
You

You define
Your world
Your life
Not me
Not anyone
You.

Sanaya Shalley (13)

Greenford High School, Southall

Empowered

Feel empowered to stand up
Feel empowered to rise against lethargy
Abandon the trail and create your own
Go your own way
For if you don't have the courage to do so
Then who will?

Feel empowered to open your eyes
Feel empowered to wonder about the future
How will it look?
How will it feel?
For if you don't have the guts to do so
Then who will?

We have to fight
Make known the dangers
That the damage is irrevocable
Feel empowered to speak out
It is our planet
It is our home
For if you don't have the spirit to do so
Then who will?

Fight or flight?

Rooda Ahmed (13)
Greenford High School, Southall

Beware Of Fortnite

People are innocent,
Fortnite is violent.
Your life is ruined,
This is an illusion.

Cars go *vroom*,
Weapons go *kablam*,
I go mad,
There goes a bang.

Building is monstrous,
Diamonds are precious,
Shooting stars are vicious,
Just like Venomous.

Klomberry is filthy,
Floppers are healthy,
John Wick is wealthy,
Just like piles of currency.

Creativity is enjoyable,
My life is miserable,
My heart is fragile,
Just like an ancient fossil.

Tilakshan Rasikanthan (13)
Greenford High School, Southall

Empowered

People follow
People hide
People disguise
People look up to others
And fail to understand why nothing turns out
The way it's supposed to
Fail to understand why
The whole world is against them.
But I know why.
If there was one thing I would sit and listen to
And take advice from
That would be my heart.
Because it is far more reliable than
My mother
My father
Or my sisters
Or my friends
Or anybody else.
If I follow my heart
I know I won't regret it later.

Karina Khar (13)
Greenford High School, Southall

Skin

What does it matter the colour of my skin?
Black, thick, thin,
When I look in the mirror, all I see,
Is another version of myself that is not me.

But what I came to realise is that my body is my own,
Different and unique,
Separate from everyone else and only belonging to me.

Everyone is different but still the same,
Our hearts identical and bodies true,
The only thing that matters is that we are all the same, our spirits connected,
Different but the same.

Hawlat Bilal (13)
Greenford High School, Southall

Idols, Hopes, Dreams, Ambitions

When I see my idol, they say,
"If you wanna get there, you've got to work hard and run the miles."

I'm working hard on my dreams but if I really want to achieve them
I've got to work hard in a team.

I really like my dream and half all hope
I need to go through hot summer and winter by wearing coats.

I have dreams, hopes and idols and mostly ambitions
for all of us, it's a mission
when we achieve. It's a competition."

Abdulbasit Bakhshi (12)
Greenford High School, Southall

You Are Unique

Do what you like
don't be in fright
and fly like a kite
if you lose hope
and you can't cope
when you're sad, tell yourself a joke
empower other people and let go of your greed
do what you desire
and don't forget, you can retire
speak up and let them hear
and always remember you will always be here
never give up, always go up
and don't let anyone stop you from working your way up
just always remember
you are unique.

Jahish Sayanthan (11)
Greenford High School, Southall

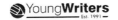

Fighting Climate Change

You better watch out,
You better not cry,
The world is ending,
And I'm telling you why,

Try riding a bike,
Try walking to school,
Try saving our planet,
And the polar bears too

Less plastic in our oceans,
Less use of electricity too,
Pick up the litter you see, walking to school.

Frances Hartnett (13)
Greenford High School, Southall

Make A Difference!

Things that matter,
in the world,
means making a difference
for other people and yourself.

So walk and lead,
don't get lost in the game,
shine your light,
make your own path.

Get your justice
and break this illusion
that has been made,
and create your own identity

Anmol Sarna (11)
Greenford High School, Southall

Did You?

Dear future self
It's your past self
Did you ever become successful?
Did you manage to keep this poem safe?
Did you choose bad or good choices?
Did you bunk school or stay?
Did you move in with Ana and Nikki?
Did you receive help?
Did you get a job
Or did you rely on your parents?
Did you raise money for charity?
Did you travel to central London with Lily or Nikki?
Did you leave your friends?
Did you listen to the visions in your head
Or did nothing you ever dreamed of?

Ashleigh Doba-Bishop (12)
Hammersmith Academy, Shepherd's Bush

Future Me

Dear future me,
Follow your dreams
No matter how bad it gets
Never give up.

Dear future me,
Don't be afraid of how you feel,
The truth burns.

Dear future me,
Smile every day
Don't let anyone bring you down.

Dear future me,
Hang around with friends and family
Tell them you love them.

Dear future me,
Live your life
Be prepared for what's going to happen.

Eileen Tazarkesh (12)
Hammersmith Academy, Shepherd's Bush

The Person That I Am

Am I the person that you can see?
Am I the person that I aspire to be?
Am I the person I am on the outside?
Or am I the person who I feel on the inside?

Am I the person who loves trampolining?
Am I the person who spends hours on gaming?
Am I the person who loves writing?
Or am I the person who loves running?

I may be the person who you see
I may be the person who I aspire to be
But keep this in mind,
This is the person I am.

Deksan Guelle (11)
Hammersmith Academy, Shepherd's Bush

Different

We are people
Some are tall
Some are small
We are not the same

We are people
Some are from deserts
Which are harsh and deadly
Some are from the countryside
Which is green and peaceful
We are not the same

We are people
We are from America, Europe, Asia
We are from all over the world
We will never be the same.

Leonard Owedye (11)
Hammersmith Academy, Shepherd's Bush

Me

Look at me
Look at you
We are different, right?
I talk my talk
You walk your walk
I don't need to walk your walk
You don't need to talk my talk
We are not sculptures to be chipped away
But to be empowered every day
We must clear the path for others
To inspire
To create
To succeed.

Mariam Kouira (11)
Hammersmith Academy, Shepherd's Bush

Don't Let People Destroy Your Dreams

Once you were a child
Dreaming about your future
And now you're an adult
Trying to conquer them
So if someone tries to stop you from doing that
Shut them off
Don't let them take time from you
Because they don't deserve it.

Leticia Delfina (11)
Hammersmith Academy, Shepherd's Bush

Our Empowerment

Stand up and speak
To inspire and seek
For all those fear towered
Needing to be empowered
Like the people I witness suffering, struggling
We can make a change for their covering and hiding.

Darne Zewldi (12)
Hammersmith Academy, Shepherd's Bush

Our Planet

I feel like our world is dying
Almost like it's crying
Endangered species, deforestation and so much pollution
We need to think of a solution
Our world is a magnificent place
Soon this will no longer be the case
Stop moaning and being drastic
We all need to stop using so much plastic
Let's begin to plant more trees
A space for animals and their families
Come to your senses and all start admitting
We're consuming too much meat, not to mention
overfishing
Let's put this to an end
This beautiful planet is our friend
For future generations to come
The work here has all been done.

Ella Williams (12)
Haydon Secondary School, Eastcote

Global Warming

G reenhouse gases
L ocking the heat in huge masses
O ur precious planet is ill
B ut there's time to save it from the real deal
A ll of us need to help Earth
L ove our planet, it needs a rebirth.

W e can prevent all of this, I'll tell you how
A nd make sure you start doing it now
R educe, reuse, recycle, it's not hard
M ore public transport, cars should be crushed
I t's not easy, but we can stop this ruthless slaughter
N ever forget your sons and daughters
G lobal warming, remember you can make a difference.

Kayden Yeung (13)
Haydon Secondary School, Eastcote

Validation

My own opinion is never enough
I need to hear others to think up
My appearance, my work, or how I am
Isn't valued if it is not heard around

Seeking reassurance, seeking validation
Is the only way to know I am sane
Pushing those away, if I don't hear what I seek
Just to be sure, I know what people think

A comment is enough, a compliment better
Because I feel safe in a space where opinions matter.

Lily Norbury (15)
Haydon Secondary School, Eastcote

If I Had The Power To Stop Global Warming

If I had the power to stop global warming I would
If I had the power to stop ice caps from melting I would
If I could stop heat waves I would
If I could stop the water from drying up I would
If I had the power to stop sea levels from rising I would
If I had the power to stop natural disasters I would
If I had the power to slow down the rate of CO2 I would
If I had the power to stop people using cars I would
If I could stop global warming killing wildlife I would
If I had the power to stop polar bears from losing their homes I would
Help stop global warming

If I had the power, I would make the government listen to Greta Thunberg
If I had the power, I would destroy people who chop down trees
I would make people bicycle or walk to work
I would make people use less electricity
I would make people use solar panels.

Leah Clarke (15)
Heath Park School, Wolverhampton

If I Had A Magic Wand, I Would...

If I had a magic wand, I would make myself invisible
If I had a magic wand, I would see the future
If I had a magic wand, I would cast a spell on you
If I had a magic wand, I would make poor people richer
If I had a magic wand, I would make myself royalty

With my magic wand, I would give myself magical powers
If my magic wand was broken, I would magic myself a new one
I would cast my wand to stick the robbers in their place
I would cast my wand to make cookies into presents
My magic wand and I would fly to the moon
I would cast my wand to destroy the pain away
I would cast my wand to spark fire out of my hands
I would cast my wand to shut windows
If I had a magic wand, I would...

Sophia Parveen (16)
Heath Park School, Wolverhampton

Power

You are you,
No one can be you,
But when someone holds you down,
Don't let them get to you.

You are strong,
You will set an example,
Don't let anyone break your spirit,
And if they do, stand up and defend what is right.

Don't be afraid to make mistakes,
Because mistakes are what make you, you,
Uplift others,
No one is perfect, we are all unique.

Help others to seek what's right,
Don't just sit there,
You have a voice,
Use it for what is right.

Simran Kaur (12)

Heath Park School, Wolverhampton

My Art Feelings

As I draw,
what comes to mind
I finally feel relieved
time to time
My imagination finally pops
this is what I wanted
A masterpiece of my choice
finally emerges
It looks like a dream
Or it makes me wanna scream
I wish people would notice
But I feel too scared
for them to judge or admire
or am I showing off?

Jashandeep Kaur (12)
Heath Park School, Wolverhampton

Bojo PM

B reaking the rules

O ld people dying alone

J uice and gin at Number 10

O ld people dying alone

P rime Minister not being a role model

M ocked everyone following the rules.

Michael Musgrave (11)

Kirk Hallam Support Centre, Kirk Hallam

I'm Fearless And Can Make The Change

Through the darkness and through the days, any word can make a change.
Abusive or violent, it can harm and frighten just like compliments can cause a smile.
In a world full of billions, millions try and make a difference.
Footballers, sportsmen, celebrities, movie stars, religious leaders and pious people all make a change.
They show that everyone can do it if they put their minds to it.
Footballers step onto the pitch with the mentality of winning as you should, every single day.
Their colour doesn't matter, neither does religion, in the hope of coming home with satisfaction.

Now imagine your younger self looking up to you now, would they recognise the person you've become?
Would they see their childhood dreams becoming true?
We all love the feeling when we feel free and confident.
It's like a red carpet being laid right in front of us.
Now make it come true. These dreams and goals.
Become the person you wish to be because in reality there's no one quite like you.

Khadijah Sufi (14)
Madrasatul Imam Muhammad Zakariya School, Bolton

My Imaginary Friend

I entered my bedroom and peeked under my bed.
I saw a lonely, abandoned figure.
I looked at it, but it looked away from me so so I told it,
"You'll be my new friend, I'm sure."
I pulled it out and cleaned off the dust and since it had no name,
I decided it would be a perfect idea to call my new friend Zane.
I would tell Zane my problems, Zane would listen to them all
And never would he interrupt when I spoke.
Though Zane never replied or never spoke back,
He never took my problems as a joke.
Unlike others.
Unlike my real friends, Zane was approachable,
It seemed I could tell him anything.
A brief summary of my day at school or something bad I did,
Zane wouldn't say a thing.
At school
There was a girl called Kelly, she never really liked Zane or me.
She would mock me and my friend Zane endlessly.
I hated it when she did that and when I told my friend Zane
I'm somehow happier and my day runs peacefully.

Every day I would talk to Zane, the contentment off the scale,
The comfort of talking to him was high.
But as the days went past and time was flying fast,
I never thought about the day I'd say goodbye.

To Zane,
You're amazing and fun, someone so approachable,
You're secretive, I tell you anything without a doubt.

But when I tried to tell Zane the best thing about him,
The pages had all run out.

My emotions I've been writing,
Because it made me feel better
And the journey of my pen will go on.
'Truly the pen is mightier than the sword'.

Juyrah Hosain (12)
Madrasatul Imam Muhammad Zakariya School, Bolton

The Day I Met Hope

Hello, I'm Negativity, I'm not a special utility
and that's why I rock the positivity,
but this girl called Hope had no time to mope
and that's why she rose to the top.
If I could ever go that high,
I'd probably ask myself why?
For I had my own bubble to stay out of trouble
and I only thought of myself as rubble.
I finally cried myself to sleep,
woke up and found my table full of food to eat.
Yet I felt full and strong,
I could fight a bull even if I knew I was wrong.
So I went to school with clear dismay,
was greeted by my mates even though I thought of them as
my prison inmates,
for school was a prison and for others a haven.
That was when I was seated with a girl,
the scent of her perfume made me hurl.
She turned to me and gave me a smile,
it made me think I could jump a mile.
She made me feel a certain vibe,
something I could not possibly describe,
we hung out for a time,
It didn't even cost a dime,
But I felt I gained something, a light in my heart
that couldn't depart,

then I realised what this feeling was
something much stronger than optimistic.
It was hope.

Sasabil Zait (12)
Madrasatul Imam Muhammad Zakariya School, Bolton

My Parents

They're always there for me and give me good advice,
They make me more powerful than I could ever get from a device.
They are the flame to my fire,
They are the heart to my soul,
They are the love that keeps me going when I am alone,
They are the light to my candle,
They are the bones to my body,
They are the feelings to my thoughts,
This is how I am exquisite,
This is how I am the way I am,
They make me feel passionate,
They bring me to the light when I am in the dark,
They are my key to success.

Unaisah Patel (12)
Madrasatul Imam Muhammad Zakariya School, Bolton

Heal The Earth

The burning sky is gasping for air,
but the people on Earth do not seem to care,
the rare days of sunny rays are mourned by all,
the world nowadays is never clean,
the trees are heard sobbing from miles away,
suffering in silence, when will this end?
The world is mad with fires all around us,
begging for the day the planet will be safe,
time isn't in our favour, let's be the saviour
and empower the planet,
let it feel like home again.

Aaisha Malji (14)
Madrasatul Imam Muhammad Zakariya School, Bolton

You Can Be...

You can be the flame to the fire,
You can be the light that makes you shine,
You can be the tissue to your tears.

You can believe in what you achieve,
You can pursue your dreams,
You can reach your goals.

Someone in your life can light that flame,
Someone in your life can shine that light,
Someone in your life can catch that tear,
Someone in your life can empower you.

Maryam Akram (12)
Madrasatul Imam Muhammad Zakariya School, Bolton

Because I Care

There was something I had to do,
But I never knew how to put it through.
I thought about it all the time,
It is always in my mind.

It is important to me because I care,
Care about the wildlife,
Care about the animals,
Care about nature.

Today is the day,
The day to pay,
The day to pay so everything is right,
So join me and bring all your might.

Bareerah Sadick (12)
Madrasatul Imam Muhammad Zakariya School, Bolton

School Transition

It's been talked about for weeks,
and now the day has come.
I give a final glance,
to my equally anxious mum.

As I make my way,
besides the car-filled roads,
with thoughts about the day ahead,
my mind overloads.

The gate's now in my view,
my heart beats like a drum,
a part of me wants to run back,
and be at home with Mum.

But I know I'm ready for this,
the next step on my journey.
Everyone is lovely here,
I can see this is the school for me.

Katie Moray (12)
Maidenhill School, Stonehouse

Environment

E   ndangered animals
N   o species are safe
V   ery vicious hunters
I   nvading forests
R   hino horns hanging on walls
O   veruse of plastic
N   ow found amongst the oceans
M   elting ice caps, water levels rising
E   ndangered polar bears aren't surviving
N   ow that nature isn't alright
T   he future isn't looking too bright.

Megan Vaughan (13)
Maidenhill School, Stonehouse

My Magic Wand

If I had a magic wand
I would change the world
I would give a cosy home
To every boy and girl

If I had a magic wand
I would save the planet
By stopping climate change
And ending world wars.

Maxine Strode (11)
Maidenhill School, Stonehouse

Mountain Biking With Family

A haiku

Mud all on my face
Flying down ramps fast as cars
Floating through the air.

Isaac Page (13)

Maidenhill School, Stonehouse

Empowered

Everyone should stand tall because if you don't, you will fall
Step out of your comfort zone
Then you will know you have a backbone
If you are alone, don't moan
Get outside and get on a phone
When we have strength, we have power
We will be beautiful like a flower
When we are empowered, we are inspired
We have ambitions and drive, like a gun fired.

Robert Clark (13)
North Herts ESC, Hitchin

The Cat

Cats don't care what kind of person you are
They don't care what you look like
They show their pride, they show you their independence
Feel their soft fur on your bare skin
And their cold nose on your face
Their love is bittersweet
They will play endlessly
They bring the pride out in you.

Ellie-May D (14)
North Herts ESC, Hitchin

Year Seven Starting 2021

Year seven starting 2021,
Two years disrupted hasn't been fun
Zoom, Teams and parents with our home school,
Hoping it sticks and we don't become fools.

Year seven starting 2021,
Oh no, apparently lots of work to be done,
Learning new subjects, maths, science, DT,
But best of all, lots of new sports in PE.

Year seven starting 2021,
Playing rugby and our team won,
We've missed concerts, field trips, plays, inter-school events,
And even sports days.

Year seven starting 2021,
Hopes, dreams and aspirations of what is to become.
Lots of new people and friends to be made,
Once was daunting, but now not afraid.

Year seven starting 2021,
Online with Google Classrooms,
All these new methods of doing homework,
Help us plan and write like clockwork.

Year seven starting 2021,
It's our time to shine and not be outdone,
Going to school, used to walk, but now on the bus,
Started as stress, but now it's no fuss.

Year seven starting 2021,
Can we last out the year and say we won?
When it's all over, we will all say it was great,
Oh wait, what do you mean, do it again in year eight?

Esme Michalec (11)
Rainford High School, Rainford

Don't Listen

They call you fat
When you are the opposite of that
They call you fat because you are better than them
Maybe it's as small as scoring a pen
But you do you and they do them
So the next time they call you fat just don't listen.

They make fun of you for nothing really
It's because they have nothing else to do clearly
Whatever it is, your glasses, accent or colour of skin
It may all make you feel like rubbish in a bin
If it all makes you feel like this just don't listen.

Levi Shaw (11)
Rainford High School, Rainford

The Changing World

The world is changing in many ways,
As we peer back at better days,
But a bird in a cage,
A bullet in a brain,
We refuse to face the present in our dismay
And nothing is where it belongs,
The past is new,
The future is old,
So we must work together and stand strong,
Because for all we know we don't have long.
There are sinking villages
And our delusional mirages
Of the world that we could live in,
Our changing world.

Francesca Jones (12)
Rainford High School, Rainford

2021

2021 was an eventful year
We lost so much
Through blood, sweat and tears.

We faced a lockdown
In our beloved hometown
Vaccinations are a waste of science
I believe this due to the lack of appliances.

We faced so much more
That we had never done before
But now it's time to say goodbye
Let's hope 2022 is the year that flies by.

Poppy Foster (13)
Rainford High School, Rainford

Climate

The Amazon rainforest, the heart of Brazil
Is the home to the animals and life
The Amazon used to be colourful and bright
But now is just derelict and dull
Poachers killing our potential hope
Our animals are dying and never coming back
The climate is going up and never coming down
Unless we do something now.

Isabella Green (12)
Rainford High School, Rainford

Positive Vibes

E mpowerment
M ake your voice heard
P ut yourself forward
O wn your dreams
W hen you fall, get back up again
E veryone is equal
R ise up and smile
M istakes happen
E ncourage others
N ever give up
T rust yourself.

Leila Bouhnassa (13)
Rainford High School, Rainford

His Hands

His hands travelled up my leg exploring the bruises he created.

His hands touched my skin making me want to scream for help.

His hands left me tossing and turning in the night.

His hands stole my confidence.

His hands took my life away.

His hands made me say, "Me too!"

Holly Herrington (15)

Rainford High School, Rainford

Cat
A haiku

Forever kitten
As playful as the sunrise
Despite your old age.

Kali Guinness (11)
Rainford High School, Rainford

Bang

Bang!

A mad dash from the line
rookies take the lead
a momentary thrill
groping at glory
but inexperience scrapes
away their gold
as they approach the first hill

spikes dig in
mud flecks fly
a leading squad takes shape
pumping arms
ploughing knees
the reins of the race
return to the pros

among them is gold
keeping pace just behind
as they ease into rhythm,
steady they stride,
biding their time...

the crest of the race
is yet to come
the final lap of the course

when the one becomes many
and every place is fought

though not yet set,
those who gave it their all
drift to the back
third to fifth
they've got nothing left.

It's the sly second place
who makes up the gap,
thanks first for their pace
and powers on past

now it's a race
the torch ripped from their hold
they motor ahead
in pursuit of the gold

neck and neck
bounding strides
hands in fists
running faster
working harder
refusing to give in!

The line approaches...
but one can't keep up.
Their fleeting glimpse of victory

slips from
their
grasp.

For the new gold
sprint becomes take-off
charging to the line
hurtling at the tape, they
burst
through the finish!

Stopping almost instantly.
It's an unsteady walk,
on quivering legs.
Token in hand,
the medal looms ahead...

Gold shines victorious
in the January sun.
Of one thousand runners,

there can be only one.

Ella Davey (15)
Ranelagh School, Bracknell

Unnamed

She sits across from me
Thank god she doesn't see
She's so pretty, all I can do is stare
It's really not fair

Sometimes I wish she knew
Just how beautiful she is
I thought about holding her
And maybe giving her a kiss

She brightens my world
She's a literal star
But I'll never tell her
I'll admire from afar

Because she already has him
And why can't she see
He's not good enough for her
Oh, why can't it be me

Who she is in love with
And spends all her day with
Why can't she look at me
Like I'm the only one she sees?

But she'll never love me
Never think twice
Because if we were together
It wouldn't be right

It's not allowed
And it's just so sad
We're just two girls in love
What's so bad?

Gabi Howe (16)
St Bernard's Catholic Grammar School, Slough

Anxiety

Anxiety, anxiety
It creeps inside of me,
It grows like a tree,
Yet no one can see

The damaged confidence,
The shaking hands,
It comes out of me like twisting strands,
Everybody seems to misunderstand.

I feel uneasy, I'm full of fear
I don't want anyone to come near.
I scream and shout, but no one can hear
They treat me like I've disappeared.

I can't order food,
I can't talk to people.
I'm not in the mood,
Talking feels illegal.

I can't sleep, I can't eat,
I can't talk, I can't speak,
I can't do things people can normally do,
I feel like I am such a fool.

Eabha McConnell (13)
St Catherine's College, Armagh

Earth's Complaining

Arctic animals are suffering
We just ignore
The ice caps are melting
We need to do something more

Imagine your house slowly faded away
You'd be in despair
The animals feel this every day
Help to get rid of the toxins in the air

Purchase electric cars
To keep the air clear
Don't burn fossil fuels
We must persevere

2022 has been an awful year
From Covid to war, it's more than we fear.

Beth Kerr (14)
St Malachy's High School, Castlewellan

Sail

Sail
Wind, rain,
Getting battered by hail,
Carry on and persevere
Calm, sun
Sail.

Ciara Cartwright (14)
St Malachy's High School, Castlewellan

Someday...

Someday you will reach your dreams
It might be harder than it seems
Someday you will have hopes
Although there will be slopes
If you persevere
You will achieve

Someday you won't need to judge
Or hold a grudge
To feel confident in who you are
Because you will go far

Someday you will laugh and love
And you will float above
All those who made you feel bad;
Someday you will realise that there is so much you can add
To life

Someday I hope you see
That you are who you're meant to be.

Emily Turner (14)
Stanborough School, Welwyn Garden City

Reality

Where do you feel most alive?
Everyone is different in their own way.
People swerve through feelings trying to escape from reality.
Where do I most feel alive?
I don't, it's hard living the same over and over again.
Reality is deep.
You come to focus on people's emotions, feelings and opinions.
Some people don't feel alive.
Why does that question even come into mind?
Some people feel alive but reality hits hard.
Sometimes people don't even know their own identity.
Identity comes with reality.
Reality goes with identity.

Tianna Parmley (13)

Stanborough School, Welwyn Garden City

Tomorrow I...

Tomorrow I will grow up
But I promise I will never give up
To give up would be dishonest
And that's why I promised

Tomorrow is a fresh start
Something that comforts my heart
And everything upsetting
Until we restart.

Tomorrow another day is done
Another day of nothing fun
Another day where life stops
And we must go on.

Oliver Kyriacou (13)
Stanborough School, Welwyn Garden City

Lost

Who am I?
Who are you?
Take that extra step
And you'll find a clue
For you could be worthy
And become something new

You may be struggling.
And continue troubling.
But keep on striving,
And you'll keep on surviving.

Matthew Ives (14)
Stanborough School, Welwyn Garden City

Don't Give Up

If you want to change the world you need to make people
hear
Don't give up and still persevere
And eventually, everything will come clear
When the road you're trudging seems uphill
Never give up because you're good enough.

When your eyes are filled with tears
Sorrowfulness is all which appears
Instead of chopping off your dreams
And ripping your life apart at the seams
Don't give up or you won't succeed.

When you're feeling blue
When the world has turned against you
And when you don't know what to do
When it pounds colossal raindrops
And you're feeling confused
Don't give up because you're good enough.

Esme Garrington-Naylor (11)
Summerhill School, Kingswinford

Calling All Gingers

Eyebrows - basically non-existent,
Eyelashes - hardly even there!
Face - pasty and white!
It's the person with the ginger hair!
Freckles may be on your face,
You will be spotted in any dull place.
I'm a ginger person - maybe you are too!
It's the person with the ginger hair!
Some say gingers are evil - but some think we are kind!
Old people seem to love gingers!
Not so much with young people you will find.
When we are called Ed Sheeren we don't mind so much -
We only care when it's our hair you try to touch.

Lucie Evans (12)
Summerhill School, Kingswinford

Resilience

As I step out of the car,
The sun rose before me,
I could feel the icy morning breeze,
Tingle against my frosty cheeks.

The mountain towered, high to sky,
No path was easy and no journey was short,
I braced myself for the path ahead,
And took one long, deep breath.

I pushed forward, step by step,
The difficulty straining my aching legs,
I climbed far and was doing great,
But my epic hike was by no means over.

Nearly there at my goal; determination set,
Scrambling up huge boulders,
My feet cold, my breath hot,
I finally reached the trig.

Resilience is the key to success,
After miles of pushing through the pain,
I was blessed with a panoramic view.
Standing on top of the world,
I had a nice cold drink.

Tyler Stocker (12)
The Manor Academy, Mansfield Woodhouse

I Am Human

How am I any different to her?
Or him?
Or them?
Is it my hair?
My eyes?
My gender?
Is it my beliefs?
My strengths?
My sexuality?
How am I different?
Why am I stereotyped?
Why are names thrown at me?
And not her?
Or him?
Or them?
I am hiding
I am crying
I am ashamed
Because of her
Him
Them
She likes boys
He likes girls
But I do too
So it's not my hair

My eyes
My beliefs
It's my sexuality
Why am I different?
I am human
I have hair, eyes, skin
I have organs, a brain and bones
Why?
How am I different?
I am human.

Isabelle Walker (12)
The Manor Academy, Mansfield Woodhouse

Life As A Teenager

It's just a phase teenagers go through,
But yet, I have no one to turn to,
All they do is sit in their room,
I feel like I'm in a tomb,

Come and talk to us, it's not that big of a deal,
My lips are sealed,
All I do is cry all night,
Hoping there is no one in sight,

What is wrong with you, child?
My head is going wild,
What's the big deal?
I don't want to go on the school bus,
So what, you have depression,
Yes, and I want to go and see a therapist and take a session.

Charlotte Hunt (12)
The Manor Academy, Mansfield Woodhouse

It's Natural

It's natural to feel hate and love
To cry and laugh
To favour ravens or doves
To mourn over memories or look back at them like old photographs

It's natural to be scared,
It's in our blood, our past
To mistrust and judge too fast
We can get filled with fear
Or with beer
And that creeping nightmare still will not go away

So, we must all remember that...

It's natural.

Denis Josu
The Manor Academy, Mansfield Woodhouse

Done This Before, Doing It Again

Been here before,
Doing it again,
End up coming back,
I know what they see in us,
They've got high expectations
It's hard but you can do it
Poem writing is easy
2019 had a hard subject
I still tried and got published in a book
Once Upon A Dream in 2019
You can do it, keep trying
Try hard, it doesn't matter
If you win or lose
Just try again the following year.

Nicola Bird (12)
The Manor Academy, Mansfield Woodhouse

Cats

Feline, graceful and elegant,
So delicate, arrogant and intelligent.
Plan their hunt with careful precision,
Making the right moves to execute their decision.
Ensuring that they are always spotless and clean,
Laying under the sun, on a soft bed of green.

Bobcats, fat cats, small cats, tomcats,
Playing hide-and-seek with portly stout rats.
Fluffy balls of furry softness,
Sitting in laps, emanating cuteness.
He cats, she cats, young cats, old cats,
Playing with balls of string on mats.

Grey, white, black and brown,
Happy with what they've found.
Crouching low on the ground,
Without making a sound.
Clever little creatures, who spin my world around,
Always bring a smile to my face when I am down.

Savannah De Sa Pinto (12)
The Sacred Heart Language College, Wealdstone

Why Does The Earth Need You

The Earth needs you to change your ways
Month by month and day by day, year by year
The changes are easy, just look and you will see the
difference that can be made
By anyone, like you and me
Our Earth is ours to enjoy for every girl and boy
But, we must all be aware of the beauty that we share
Single-use plastics may be cheap, but they aren't very clever
When they set into the sea and kill our animals
With the air that's clean and clear
For us all to breathe, year by year, month by month and day
by day

We must never abuse our loving planet Earth
That's ours to use
Act now and be the change we want to see.

Maisie Joyce-Gourey (11)
The Sacred Heart Language College, Wealdstone

Never Give Up

Tension, tension and tension was in the air.
Barcelona were 3-0 up, it was over
Unless something astonishing could happen
Something so astonishing, it would go down in history.

The whistle blew and it was live
Divock Origi with a tap-in during the seventh minute gave us hope
Half-time substitute Georginio Wijnaldum with two goals
3-3, the score was 3-3, could we score?

Trent's cheeky corner caught Barcelona off guard,
Allowing the unmarked Origi to score a goal to take
Liverpool to the final!
That's the goal that Liverpool needed,
Never give up, because anything is possible.

Simran Kaur Dhami (14)
The Sacred Heart Language College, Wealdstone

You Are To Me

You gave women hope,
To be what they want to be,
To have a career,
To do what they love.

You gave them power,
You gave them strength,
You gave them time,
You gave them the ability,
You told them to listen to themselves.

You gave them a home,
You helped them to rest,
You gave them advice,
You always thought the best of them.

You are and always will be,
The person who inspires me,
And for that,
For everything,
I want to say, thank you.

Francesca Wozniak (11)
The Sacred Heart Language College, Wealdstone

Why Do I Look The Way I Do?

She's been orbiting like a dark star
For too long
Caught in her own cloudy gravity

You see people on the street, wondering
Why you don't look pretty, but they're pretty
You look at your reflection
Wishing you could change your appearance

But now, she's free
She has the strength to rise from her pain
To smile when you're angry

To try again after failing
The strength to say you love them when life is bad.

Esioneh Adjerese (13)
The Sacred Heart Language College, Wealdstone

Supermum

To my mum and all of the mums out there

You gave me a part of you every day
you put your life on hold and held it with a rope
you helped me with my struggles
so, there's one thing I want to say to you
thank you for everything that you've done
when you homeschooled me, you were like Supermum
when I have problems, you're always there for me
and when I cried, you held my hand
so, thank you, and also, I love you more than the universe.

Inieya Haroon (11)
The Sacred Heart Language College, Wealdstone

The Emerald Isle

This is my country
The Emerald Isle
My love for it goes more than a mile
The only place I feel at home
And a phrase I can say is 'pog mo thon'

This is my country
My sweet homeland
You can find beaches with rocks or golden sand
The land that spreads far and wide
And the beautiful rhythm of the tide

This is my country
A country full of pride
Where the day of the All-Ireland, we take it in our stride.

Caitlin Byrne (14)
The Sacred Heart Language College, Wealdstone

We Shall

We shall leave the past
Behind us
Although it went by so fast
We shall dream high
Until we achieve
Don't let your dreams die
We shall walk on a path where we praise one another
A path of our dreams
Where we don't humiliate each other
We shall spread goodness throughout the world
Making it a better place to live in
Be bold
We shall welcome the future
Yet to come
Which we shall venture.

Fathimaladana Jawahirismail (11)
The Sacred Heart Language College, Wealdstone

Justice

Don't wear this and don't wear that, they all scream and
shout
Don't talk back and sit up right, what's that all about
Society wants women to sit back and suffer in silence
Why are we teaching young girls that they have to put up
with violence?
The way we are treated is vile, disgusting and wrong
Why is it hard to let us have freedom, this battle for justice
is prolonged.

Alyssa Patel (14)
The Sacred Heart Language College, Wealdstone

Plastic

It's destroying the world, that's not fun
It's eating up our oceans and seas
So, don't you see
Plastic
We need change, there are a range of solutions
So, which one do we pick?
Plastic
It's destroying our Earth from the inside out
From erupting volcanoes to big forest fires
Plastic
What shall we do to stop plastic from taking over the world?

Teodora Olariu (12)
The Sacred Heart Language College, Wealdstone

Poem To My Future Self

Dear future me,
One thing I ask of you,
Don't change yourself to make others happy,
Because you are perfect just the way you are.

Dear future me,
I ask of you one thing,
Follow your dreams,
As I know you will succeed.

Dear future me,
One thing I ask of you,
Remember to be happy every day,
Behind the mask too.

Ashita Bhuva (11)
The Sacred Heart Language College, Wealdstone

Empowered

The word empowered can be described in many ways
From the heart, from the soul, from the words that you gave
Be powered by the words of those around you
Be inspired
Break down every chain you think is holding you down
Be empowered
Take a leap of faith
Encourage others
Because at the end of the day
Our power is ours.

Jennifer Adubofour (12)
The Sacred Heart Language College, Wealdstone

Inspired

Are you inspired?
No, I am just tired
No, I have no power
Are you inspired?
No, I have no faith
Where is the inspiration?
It is in our hearts?
In our brain
And our actions?
We act
We inspire
And then we repeat
But answer my question
Are you inspired?

Gabriela Kaczorowska (12)
The Sacred Heart Language College, Wealdstone

Sexism: A Spoken Poem

The expectations between men and women are so different.
Women cannot wear what they'd like to without being
shamed for it.
They can't wear things like dresses that are just that inch
too short
Or people would say they were... 'asking for it'.

They are objectified and treated like toys,
It's almost as if they don't even exist in society anymore,
Like they aren't seen as a person.

While on the other side of the spectrum, men.
Men can't be seen as 'weak' or 'powerless',
They have to be seen as strong and independent as they
can possibly be in the eyes of society
But that isn't always the case.
They can't show any emotion that makes them appear as
they are upset or vulnerable.
Men 'must' show that they are fearless.
They can't cry or show any emotion that isn't happiness.

Men are depicted as those that should be confident and not
insecure.
But all of these things are incredibly unrealistic.

It's sexist!

Isabel Heywood (13)
The Winsford Academy, Winsford

Covid-19

The environment is tidy,
The environment is chaotic,
Children at the park screaming and having fun.
Teachers teaching!
Children playing!
People walking!
People talking!
Covid messing up everything in 2020.
Still with us after two years.
Go away!
Go away!
Everyone is saying
Lockdowns, masks, sanitisers.
Our environment in 2020, 2021 and 2022 still is torture.
No teachers!
No staff!
Getting ill.
Staying off.
Businesses closed.
Schools closed.
Worrying to not give it to parents or carers.
We need a different *generation!*

Bob Ross (14)
The Winsford Academy, Winsford

To Be...

Startled, frantic,
Petrified, dismayed,
I hide in my covers,

At the end of the day,
I miss you,
In every single way,
My soul crumbles,
And my heart grows dark,

My door creaks open,
And there you are,
Standing there still,
My heart stops,

Please never leave,
My side again,
As life without you,
I may as well be dead,

And like always,
I imagined it,
Why can't life be easy?
"It's like I'm happy for a minute then I'm sad again!"

The nights are long,
The days long between the nights.

I fall asleep,
In your arms,
Where I want to be,
Where I've always wanted...

To be.

Layla Ventre (13)
The Winsford Academy, Winsford

Remember Yourself

When you start losing yourself,
In huge and noisy crowds,
Trusting people for who you believe they are,
Rather than who they say they are,
Believing in kindness and compassion so much,
You start to think that every human,
You meet is as kind as compassionate as you are,

Just remember,

When you find yourself,
Slipping away into the pit of darkness,
After you thought you conquered all your demons,
Feeling anxious before making an order,
Even when you have rehearsed it ten times,
Pouring your heart out to a stranger,

But making enemies out of all the people you know.

Maisie Middleton (13)
The Winsford Academy, Winsford

The World

T ons of plastic in our oceans
H elpless and starving polar bears
E lectricity from polluting power stations

W orried what will happen next
O nly we can save the world from climate change
R ising temperatures of our oceans
L akes and rivers riddled with rubbish
D amaging our environment.

Adam Rowntree (13)
The Winsford Academy, Winsford

Transgender

I am only a child but hear me out,
I am who I am without a doubt,
I am forced into society's concept
Of femininity with dresses and make-up
They do not appeal to me.
My name is Cody and I'm only 11,
But the body I was born in,
It just isn't me.
I am transgender,
And I'm filled with glee,
That finally,
I can be free.

Cody Elliot (12)
The Winsford Academy, Winsford

Empowered Future Me

I have so many questions for you.
Like, when does Coronavirus end?
Or how much homework do you get in sixth form?
I'll be able to read this later but for now this letter is just pretend.
What empowered you to stand where you are now?
Was it some guy or a school visitor
Or were you never empowered at all?
Like a locked up, sad and hopeless prisoner.
I hope you were empowered so I can be empowered later in life.
I hope you didn't end up as a failure when you rolled the dice.
You probably did become empowered in your adult life.
Unlike some homeless guy who is too sad to be nice.
In the future, if you're empowered then I'm empowered.
And if you're happy then I'm happy as well.
Do I become a doctor in my later life
Or do I become a well cleaner who got stuck in a dirty well?
In the future, am I able to control my temper
Or does my temper get me sentenced to death?
Am I a parent in life?
I hope we are a man of empowerment.
Sincerely,
Past you.

Lucas Tottman (12)
Torquay Boys' Grammar School, Torquay

Odd Street

There is a statue on the fourth street
'Tis of a king from years passed
The statue has been beat
By nature's power

He used to empower the people
He used to oppress people
He used to scare them
And they couldn't bear him
So off with his head

There is a new statue at 4th
Not of a king, nor a queen
But the oddest fellow you'd ever seen
His plaque read
'The man who never went to bed'
The poet who wrote it
Would always gloat it
So, it became Odd Street.

Felix Kelly (12)
Torquay Boys' Grammar School, Torquay

Don't Judge

It's not fair
To be oppressed
It can feel so bad
Like a hole through your chest
Bullying someone for what they believe
Is hard to even conceive
How people can be so horrible
To make someone feel so down
So many negative thoughts they could drown
When really everyone deserves a crown
Someone is wrong because of their race
Is something you should never say
For their race, beliefs or even if they're gay
Everyone is even
Even if you're called Steven.

Tyler Piercey (12)
Torquay Boys' Grammar School, Torquay

Encourage

Be inspired
Be brave
Be *you*
You are you
You are perfect

No matter what some bullies say
No matter if you and your friend had an argument

The light inside you may fade
But don't mourn and tear and fear and pain
Work harder and spread your love to people like you again

The tough and strong
May make you feel gone
All the happiness and sadness may make you ball up and
cry
But the light inside you will never fail to shine.

Joe Day (12)
Torquay Boys' Grammar School, Torquay

Nature

The trees, the bees, all keep us at ease
Help us thrive just like a tree, without them we couldn't
breathe,
We do, we see, but are blinded by greed,
We do what gives money but not what gives us glee,
We need to care, we need to see beyond the greed
Because we can make a change and
A change it will be.
We stand tall together and we can see
The saviour we can be.

Jaden Sanders-Yeoman (12)
Torquay Boys' Grammar School, Torquay

Friends

Me, oh me, I feel alive when
I'm with my friends
support and comfort
when I need it
friends are needed
everywhere.

Imagine a world
without friends
where no one
was content

That's why
next time
you see
your friends
remember what
the world
would be like
without them.

Isaac Rollings (11)
Torquay Boys' Grammar School, Torquay

School

School
Playing and learning
But the mind is always turning
On what we want to achieve in life
Only the people that are bright
Will fulfil their massive dream
But it could not be as it seems
Five periods a day
Five days in a week
One hundred and ninety days a year.

Hoyt Spencer (12)
Torquay Boys' Grammar School, Torquay

Forgotten

Reaching a standstill at all the lost memories,
Figuring out for centuries.
Inevitable.

Crippling depression lurks on my mind,
Yet nothing to bind.
Understandable.

Grasping onto a concept that is not needed,
Numerous thoughts deleted.
Irreplaceable.

Trying to piece together that idea, searching endlessly,
However, the door would not open like a sesame.
Relatable.

A fear amongst many.
Give or take...

Aryan Vekaria (12)
Wembley High Technology College, Wembley

The Phone

On the bed I lie,
Waiting for the alarm,
It goes off,
My owner Waled leaves me on snooze!
As I keep ringing and ringing

He wakes up, checks the time
As I cry,
He is like a goldfish
And he leaves me in his blazer
For six hours!
As I am off with no purpose
Every day I think maybe he will treat me right!
But he does not.

Waled Alsabah (11)
Wembley High Technology College, Wembley

War Some More

War and war some more.
War and war some more.
No one knows
What it's for,
War and war some more.

The images seem
To rule the day,
War and generals
All the same,
All the answers
Seem so lame,
All our reason,
Gone insane.
War and war some more.

Daria Maxinese (12)
Wembley High Technology College, Wembley

YOUNG WRITERS INFORMATION

We hope you have enjoyed reading this book – and that you will continue to in the coming years.

If you're the parent or family member of an enthusiastic poet or story writer, do visit our website **www.youngwriters.co.uk/subscribe** and sign up to receive news, competitions, writing challenges and tips, activities and much, much more! There's lots to keep budding writers motivated!

If you would like to order further copies of this book, or any of our other titles, then please give us a call or order via your online account.

Young Writers
Remus House
Coltsfoot Drive
Peterborough
PE2 9BF
(01733) 890066
info@youngwriters.co.uk

Join in the conversation!
Tips, news, giveaways and much more!

 YoungWritersUK    YoungWritersCW    youngwriterscw